WEIGH
YOUR
OPTIONS

Maurie,

Good luck to you in your future career. Your natural compassion and love of life will serve you and your clients well.

Dr. Pat

WEIGH
YOUR
OPTIONS

PERSONAL POWER
in
NUTRITION & HEALTH

DR. PATRICIA M.
CASELLO

Andover,
Minnesota

ISBN 1-931945-03-9

Library of Congress Catalog Number: 2002117360

Printed in the United States of America

First Printing: January 2003

06 05 04 03   6 5 4 3 2 1

Expert Publishing, Inc.
14314 Thrush Street NW,
Andover, MN 55304-3330
1-877-755-4966
www.expertpublishinginc.com

*Andover,
Minnesota*

DEDICATION

God, give us grace to accept with serenity the things that cannot be changed, courage to change the things which should be changed, and the wisdom to distinguish the one from the other.

—Reinhold Niebuhr, *American Theologian 1892-1971*

CONTENTS

FOREWORD
ACKNOWLEDGEMENTS

I have been a holistic health and spiritual practitioner since the mid 1980s. Through the years, I continue to discover a universal link between health, health choices, and stages of internal power. As you read this book, take time to become aware of any emotions and thoughts that arise from self-reflection. Judgments and tendencies to place blame on you or others are not uncommon and emotional backlash often accompanies personal growth. This is a sign of successful movement forward, especially if we work with, rather than against, change.

This book examines the six stages of personal power in health choices. Each chapter details a different stage. Each stage has an identifying name and definition, physical symptoms and characteristics (ingredients), a health crisis that creates a need for change or is the by-product of an ignored need to change, a shadow side ("misfortune cookies") that holds us back, a "golden shadow" of beneficial character strengths, and ways to successfully move forward. Personal stories are given as examples although the names have been changed to protect the individual's privacy.

As you read through each chapter, you will find a series of questions preceding each of the six sections. Personal power stages one through three are closely aligned with external symbols that are more tangible. They ask the questions, "Will things ever get better?", "What is in it for me?", and "How does this affect me?" Stages four through six begin to address the questions, "What is my life purpose?", "How do I achieve my life purpose?", and "How do I best serve others?"

The early stages generally have more concrete questions because these stages are more easily aligned with visible, external symbols and rewards. Also, there may be more denial at an earlier stage. Stages four and beyond become a deeper, internal journey where the motivation is intangible and spiritually tied. The questions help us identify our dominant personal power stage, as well as crossover, adjacent stages. If you find yourself answering "yes" to many of the questions for a given chapter, you probably identify strongly with that stage. Identifying with a stage allows you to thoughtfully examine your life goals, review possible obstacles, and move forward successfully. There is no right or wrong stage for each of us. Honestly accepting a current stage is the best way to move forward. You can be in different stages at different times in your life. You will move through them, perhaps quickly, maybe backsliding or repeating stages at times. You may not go through all of the stages in a lifetime. Life is a process and so is health. The important thing is to continue moving through the stages to your eventual destination in this lifetime.

I give great thanks to the many who have come before me, paving the way for my knowledge and my personal growth. These include, but are not limited to, the Real Power Network, Janet Hagberg and her model for the six stages of personal power; the Living in Process elders, training, and groups; the building knowledge of energy anatomy, psychoneuroimmunology, and psychoneuroendocrinology; Jack Caravella and Jay Monroe at Mori Studio for their design work; Sharron and Harry Stockhausen of Expert Publishing for their editing and publishing expertise; National Speakers Association members; Michael Chiodi and Janet Berryhill for their greatly appreciated business coaching and support; the shared experience, strength, and hope of my sponsor, Judy H.; many twelve-step people, and recovery programs; Kevin Fenton for his creative "misfortune cookies"; Tom Tuttle for his loving friendship and collegial support; and the support of family, friends, and clients. I found my teachers in the most unusual niches and the most conspicuous places. As my life unfolds in spiritual experiences, the meaning of "pass it on" and "pay it forward" become increasingly more clear. This writing is an effort to honor that shared knowledge. May you find peace, health, and harmony on your personal journey.

INTRODUCTION

I have worked in several industries over the years. In each, I have been a teacher. As a holistic doctor, I find that I am again a teacher. As I worked one-on-one with my clients, or in a group setting with students, I discovered a set of responses that at first seemed random. As I became better acquainted with my clients and students, I found their commitment to spiritual growth and healing on all levels affected by their beliefs regarding personal power. My work has been built upon the shoulders of countless others who have been my spiritual teachers and guides through the years. My own life has been transported through the first four personal power stages in recurring patterns as I have improved my self-care, changed careers, and explored my life options.

The personal power stages are a progressive spiritual awakening of knowing about our life purpose and how to carry that out. Our life purpose is often different from what we want it to be or even think it should be. My life's purpose is to teach from my experience. This knowing will grow and evolve in future years.

As a holistic practitioner, I see the forward movement, plateau, or abandonment of health goals in all realms. This process is normal and is approached differently by each person. The same person approaches life's choices differently throughout their lifetime. No individual stage is good or bad. Actually, judging a particular stage is a wonderful way to remain stuck at an individual step. This is part of our shadow side or what my good friend, Kevin, calls the "misfortune cookies" - that internal urge to self-sabotage ourselves.

Do not be discouraged wherever you are on the journey. This book is an encouraging blueprint for you. Although you cannot predict every twist and turn of your path, you can ease the way by focusing your attention and choices. From there the steps become purposeful and attainable if you are willing to move beyond your own obstacles. Twelve-step members pray to a higher power to "relieve me of the bondage of self." Caroline Myss' work in energy anatomy has individuals look at what archetypal systems they relate to in terms of specific values and limitations; she also encourages people to explore what spiritual sacred contracts drive their behaviors and lives. Whatever model you choose as a reference point, confronting the "misfortune cookies" of your shadow side is the greatest challenge and spiritual reward.

Stage One: *Fast Food*

Please answer the questions in the following checklist:

Yes No

❏ ❏ Do you want your life to be different but feel there is nothing that you can do about your diet, your weight, your energy, or general health?

❏ ❏ Do you feel that repeated attempts to make a change will only fail?

❏ ❏ Do you feel that no one can or will help you?

❏ ❏ Do you believe that to have something done you have to do it yourself?

❏ ❏ Do you believe that the world (neighborhood, school, workplace, etc.) is a dangerous place?

Yes No

❏ ❏ Do you feel that you do not know what to do, where to go, or who to turn to for information and answers?

❏ ❏ Are you ashamed of your eating habits, your body, or other personal aspects?

❏ ❏ Do you crave foods or beverages that you know make you feel unwell?

❏ ❏ Do you feel that you are trapped by your circumstances: work hours, your family's needs, illness, or special circumstances?

❏ ❏ Are you afraid to take responsibility for decisions regarding your health?

❏ ❏ Do you abdicate decision-making regarding your health to others— your doctor, partner, children, relatives, or friends?

Yes No

❏   ❏   Do you question your self-worth? Do you feel unworthy of feeling fit or looking healthy?

❏   ❏   Do you dislike yourself?

❏   ❏   Does taking a risk make you anxious?

❏   ❏   Have your past attempts on your own been unsuccessful?

❏   ❏   Have you tried controlling what you eat, drink or do, negotiating with yourself and feeling shame if you lose control?

❏   ❏   Do you diet, starve, purge, or over-exercise to offset your eating habits?

❏   ❏   Do you believe that if you were the right size, shape or perfect weight, your life would be better?

❏   ❏   Do you eat to escape problems or to relieve boredom?

Yes No

❏ ❏ Do you feel that others do not respect you?

❏ ❏ Do you believe that life would be better if others just did what you wanted them to do?

❏ ❏ Do you misrepresent what, how much, where, or when you eat?

❏ ❏ Have your choices in nutrition led to self-defeating consequences such as being overweight, vomiting, or being ill with diseases such as anorexia or bulimia?

❏ ❏ Do you know little or nothing about nutrition and health in general?

❏ ❏ Do you fear physical or emotional confrontation from family, friends or others if you change things about yourself and your lifestyle, including eating habits?

Yes No

❏ ❏ Do you think something or someone else is to blame for your situation such as past events, parents, partners, or life circumstances?

❏ ❏ Are you critical or judgmental of others?

❏ ❏ Are you unable or afraid to admit when you are wrong?

❏ ❏ Do you seek the approval of others?

❏ ❏ Do you feel overwhelmed and confused when asked to make decisions regarding your health?

❏ ❏ Do you feel easily manipulated into eating or drinking what others want you to have, even when you do not really want it?

❏ ❏ Do you ever try to manipulate others to eat or drink what you want them to have?

Yes No

❏   ❏   Do you feel discriminated against in
terms of how you look or what you do?

*If you answer "Yes" to many of the questions above, it
indicates that you align yourself with stage one.*

WHAT IS STAGE ONE?

Stage one is the stage of powerlessness.
Everyone feels powerless at times. Some people feel
powerless most or all of the time. Do you pray for
weight loss or a different body image without praying for ways to change your eating and lifestyle
behaviors? Without praying for ways to love and
accept you? Without trusting that a higher spiritual
power or others can help you in this regard? Do you
eat to feel better, to feel numb, to feel less depressed,
or to feel less tired? Food does have energetic properties and reactions on the body. Junk food with
high sodium and saturated fat content or artificially
and highly sweetened products, is consumed at bil-
lions of dollars for good reason. Junk food choices

are not necessarily the best tasting food, and certainly not the most nutritious food, but they provide a temporary and much needed emotional lift or balancing in stage one. On a metaphysical level this relates to physical, emotional, and spiritual issues surrounding 1) family, 2) physical safety, security, and support in the world, and 3) feelings of hopelessness and helplessness.

This is the FAST FOOD approach to health. Whatever takes the least amount of time, energy, and money to temporarily and quickly feel better, look better, or find a "fix" for life's problems is often the first choice. We fuel unhealthy decisions by the perceived scarcity of resources and a feeling of hopeless resignation. We fuel healthy choices by gathering information and courage for personal decisions toward health, vitality, and peace of mind.

STAGE ONE INGREDIENTS

The characteristics are:

- Feelings of fear, helplessness, and resignation—I cannot do this. No one will help me.

- Egocentric, but distrustful self-dependence—If I want it done, I have to do it myself. I will probably fail. It will not be good enough.

- Fear and distrust—The world is a dangerous place. People and circumstances are not dependable.

- Lack of information or knowledge—I do not know what to do or where to go.

- Dependent, focusing on others' needs while neglecting our own needs—Their needs are more important than mine.

- Low self-esteem, criticism of ourselves, self-focused in a negative, judgmental way; putting ourselves down; comparing ourselves as less than—What is the matter with me? Others can do this. Why can't I lose weight? (Stop smoking? Quit drinking?)

- Lack of information, not having or gathering information to make decisions nor to see options—I don't have a choice.

WHAT HOLDS US BACK?

The "misfortune cookies" of this stage are:

- Fear and ego head the list. Stage one people will often see themselves as victims or become so frustrated by their circumstances that they become either 1) withdrawn, or 2) demanding and manipulative to get what they want because they cannot see any other options.

- Loyalty to the status quo may be a problem. Loyalty is a good trait to ensure community cohesion, a sense of belonging and security. It can also blindly bind us to old patterns that are not helpful. Family and cultural norms about food and eating can help trap many people into continuing patterns that are harmful to them.

Even well intentioned statements and questions about attempts to change may be interpreted as an indication that we are outside the norm, different, and unacceptable. To move past this requires courage and support to challenge family, community, and cultural norms or traditions when they are no longer useful.

- A lack of a true sense of honor can be harmful. This involves trusting yourself and keeping your commitments to yourself and others. If you do not have a consistent, internal reference framework to work from, life seems vulnerable and unpredictable. In addition, upholding a value system that you do not believe in leaves you feeling ambivalent and unsure of yourself and others.

- Common areas of physical symptoms related to these "misfortune cookies" are chronic low back pain, hemorrhoids, rectal problems, varicose veins, menstrual problems, sexual problems, and depression. Although these problems may occur in other stages, they are often found problematic in this stage. The good news is that these same symptoms, which create a life crisis for us, are also our motivation to move forward and beyond the crisis.

WHAT PROMOTES CHANGE?

- A change in self-esteem—People begin to view themselves differently; they see the possibility of being lovable and having purpose.

- An increase in knowledge—There is a gathering of information and viable choices.

- A need to develop skills personally or professionally—Stage one people will begin to unlearn old, ineffective behaviors while learning and repeating useful new behaviors.

STAGE ONE STORIES

Debbie is a young woman with chronic back problems. A recent automobile collision magnified her back pain and discomfort. Always fatigued, she also admitted that she did not eat very much nor very well. As she improved, I periodically made comments on her progress. Every time I told her she was getting better and we should increase her daily self-care routine and reduce the frequency of her visits, she had another accident. I began to wonder if her fear of getting better and being self-reliant was more potent than the possibility of living in constant pain.

Pam experienced a vicious cycle of eating disorders, depression, suicide, drug dependency, and alcoholism. Most of the time she could not see her cycle of repetitive self-destructive behaviors. Even when she was aware, she turned to highly fantastical rationalizations for these continued actions. She did not trust people and saw almost everyone's actions as "out to get her." She was extremely bright, which complicated the process because she relied on her own thoughts and perceptions to resolve her difficulties. This, of course, kept resulting in the same outcome—a return to self-destructive patterns.

WHERE DO WE GO FROM HERE?
HOW DO WE MOVE TO STAGE TWO?

Try these suggestions:

- Admit powerlessness. The paradox is that we find a greater resolve and strength to work with when we face our weaknesses and problems.

- Build self-esteem. Find yourself and appreciate your strengths. Large or small, our contributions have an impact in this world.

- Build support systems. Find like-minded people. Share your feelings and experiences for support.

- Develop appreciation of yourself and life. Create a gratitude list and keep adding to it.

- Confront yourself and fear. Be honest about past and present behaviors. "Hit your bottom."

- Become willing to live. Most people choose not to die. Some choose a slow route toward death through self abuse. A few choose to truly live.

Moving from stage one to two requires learning that we are teachable, changeable, and lovable after all. This is often first known by our mind or intellect. Later we incorporate this on a much deeper level. It is a long journey from our head to our heart. It is even longer to our soul and well worth the effort.

CHAPTER 2

Stage Two: *Community Buffet*

Please answer the questions in the following checklist:

Yes   No

❏   ❏   Do you imitate others in behavior, dress, habits, or body image?

❏   ❏   Are you using role models, mentors, coaches, or sponsors?

❏   ❏   Do you compare "your insides to other people's outsides"?

❏   ❏   Do you feel that you are beginning to learn the rules of the game or to grasp "the program"?

❏   ❏   Are you loyal to a group, a sponsor, a mentor, or others that support you and your developing skills and choices?

Yes No

❏ ❏ Are most of your contacts through groups and support networks?

❏ ❏ Do you like being around the "experts," or people in positions of authority, power, or perceived knowledge?

❏ ❏ Do you believe that your doctor, nurse, healthcare professional, or government agency has all the answers?

❏ ❏ Are you beginning to know yourself?

❏ ❏ Do you seek advice from as many people and as many sources as possible?

❏ ❏ Are you joining gyms for group exercise?

❏ ❏ Are you working with a personal trainer?

❏ ❏ Are you joining clubs and groups for dieting?

Yes No

❏ ❏ Are you taking classes on personal nutrition?

❏ ❏ Have you tried hypnosis to stop eating compulsively, to quit overeating, or to alter some other behavior?

❏ ❏ Do you fast to lose weight?

❏ ❏ Have you tried stomach stapling, ear stapling, acupuncture, dietary aids, herbs, homeopathic remedies, Bach flower remedies, essential oils, medications, or other methods to alter your eating and behavioral habits?

❏ ❏ Do you focus on others' faults and wrongdoings, thinking about how they should improve their lives rather than focusing on how to change your own?

Yes No

☐ ☐ Are you coming to believe in a power greater than yourself whether that is God, goddess, universal energy, or your support group itself?

☐ ☐ Do you pray for help with your health concerns?

If you answer "Yes" to many of the questions above, it indicates that you align yourself with stage two.

WHAT IS STAGE TWO?

Stage two is the personal power stage of relationships and associations. As we grow in faith and choices, we rely on and trust others to guide us toward our goals. We look for expertise and experts. We follow viable suggestions and processes. Supportive people, organizations, and groups can be very useful here. In stage two, we are developing new skills, behaviors, and ways of looking at the world. Being surrounded by others who value us and support our efforts is invaluable at this stage.

The underlying belief is that if we follow the sage advice of those who have the information, we will profit from it in terms of our health, vitality, and quality of life.

The challenge of this stage may seem to be the detection of who is truly trustworthy as an information source and who has a personal agenda. The biggest lesson, though, is learning to trust our own intuition about these choices. As we begin to trust ourselves, we are able to discern the trustworthiness of those around us. We move through stage two by being apprentices of our health choices and becoming our own individual advocate. The need for mentoring relationships changes from a definition of a subordinate position to one of a collaborative effort surrounding health choices.

STAGE TWO INGREDIENTS

The characteristics are:

- A growing interest in self-knowledge, acquiring skills, and adopting change through reading, taking classes, talking to others, and joining health clubs or other organizations.

- The building of faith that others can and will help us allows us to reach out to others for assistance. Our personalized view of a higher, helping power or energy is of value here.

- A dependence on mentors, sponsors, and perceived experts for the answers to our health. Our teachers are everywhere. Watch for them in familiar and inconspicuous places.

- A need to place ourselves in a different environment or culture to test our assumptions, and to stretch ourselves. Traveling and eating in another culture or placing ourselves in an entirely different environment (i.e. gym, diet program) gives perspective to the diversity of options open to us. Our personal discovery of abundance becomes clearer.

- A sense of being "stuck." You may be stuck or simply moving slowly. Your weight loss has reached a plateau or your old physical symptoms (low energy, cravings, weight gain) have returned. People get easily discouraged here. Even if you feel that you are moving forward, it is at a slower pace than you would like.

WHAT HOLDS US BACK?

The "misfortune cookies" of this stage are:

- Trying to do it alone. Those who have emerged from stage one may have had to rely on their own resources as survival measures. Since these behaviors have proven successful in the immediate past, they are hard to give up now.

- Stopping the process too soon. Clients sometimes begin the process of healthy change only to sabotage their efforts. People do not reach success according to their own self-imposed or others' dictated timeframes. They find themselves slipping back into old behaviors. Shame and self-judgment can then stop all attempts to make and/or maintain successful changes. In twelve-step groups this may be a reluctance to work the third step or a fall from the "pink cloud" phase of early recovery. The loss of faith for those dieting, changing body image, or making physical health changes, results in a return to the previous, destructive behavior pattern with certain results and consequences. A feeling of giving up and futility can abound here. Twelve-step programs refer to this as a "slip" or relapse. Coming back into recovery the second (or more) time is often harder because of the associated shame. Repeated attempts and failures can set up a pattern of self-fulfilling defeat.

- Remaining in an environment that does not support your efforts for change. If a particular group is not lending itself to your growth, expand your support system. Staying in the same comfortable, supported position can deter growth. To move forward requires taking risk, moving away from, beyond, or changing a relationship over time. One of my shifts came when I realized I had become a good friend of a prior therapist, Vicki. I valued her input but no longer felt bound by her words nor needed her approval or agreement.

• Constantly changing groups and support systems. This may indicate an unwillingness to really examine who we are. We may feel reluctant and ambivalent about making choices for our health and wellness. Examples of this include the constant change of fad diets, exercise regiments, careers, living situations, partners, spiritual communities, and/or other areas of our lives. This is referred to as "making a geographic" or constantly being involved in change to divert attention from the real issue—our own personal commitment to internal change. This constant alteration of external things creates crisis. It also creates an outpouring of internally produced chemicals that slow our digestive process. These chemicals overtax our bodies, our mind, and our energy. People who make constant changes, and are unable to reach their goals or find internal peace may find that they are operating in their shadow side of stage two. I have often seen this happen in twelve-step groups, therapy groups, counseling, exercise programs, and various nutritional programs.

The constant change phenomenon is different from people who are high risk-takers or have a natural affinity for diverse interests. The difference here is these people reach their goals and move on from an internal sense of spiritual challenge and growth instead of searching for a quick fix to their problems. Twelve-step groups call the latter the "easier, softer way."

- Perceiving loss of control can result in physical symptoms. These "misfortune cookies" include urinary problems, pelvic and low back pain, reproductive problems, colitis, diverticulosis, and other bowel or sexual organ dysfunction.

WHAT PROMOTES CHANGE?

- We begin to trust the "kindness of strangers" and familiar people alike. Reach out to those you find most trustworthy. Practice trust in slow and incremental steps.

- We learn the paradox of letting go and the reliance on a higher power to release and remove cravings or repetitive, destructive behaviors. The long-term goal is to restore internal peace and sanity for the ease of future healthy choices.

- Instead of assuming that a given process did not work, we examine what went wrong, why it went wrong, and try again with corrective changes in place. We fine tune the process and then start again. Most successful change requires multiple attempts. I quit smoking cigarettes twenty years ago after four years and four serious attempts. They say that on average it takes 2-3 attempts to quit. Perhaps I was greater than average. Perhaps you are too.

- We continue to gain self-esteem and to develop skills by unlearning old, harmful behaviors and by learning and repeating new, helpful behaviors.

STAGE TWO STORIES

Cathy was in the middle of a detoxification and elimination diet program to examine food sensitivities. She felt better and almost completed the process when she started binge eating and drinking the offending foods and beverages.

Jennifer collected saliva samples over a period of a month to test hormone levels for various reproductive problems. She forgot to take several important samples resulting in skewed results that made her tests invalid.

Justin periodically drank coffee and ate nightshade vegetables like tomatoes, potatoes, green peppers, and eggplant. He knew these would aggravate his reflux and spastic bowel symptoms. He understood the connection between eating these foods and suffering his symptoms, but was not ready or able to give up these substances. This is an indication of knowledge without willingness. He was stuck at this stage.

These people were totally baffled by their own behavior. I asked each of them to look at what was going on in their life and how they felt just prior to and at the time they were engaging in the harmful behaviors. I also asked them to address questions about their faith in themselves and others. By pinpointing their specific "triggers," they established awareness and new guidelines for their next attempt. By reviewing their questions of faith, they opened the door for willingness to let go and to take a "leap of faith" beyond their current behaviors and beliefs.

WHERE DO WE GO FROM HERE? HOW DO WE MOVE TO STAGE THREE?

Try these suggestions:

- Continue your personal journey of self-knowledge. Read, take classes, and explore hobbies and interests in new groups.

- Stage two is a time of building faith in yourself and others. You realize you can succeed. Most successful change comes after repeated attempts and requests of help from others. These efforts can be useful if you are willing to examine each failed attempt for ways to improve your next effort rather than submerging yourself in self-recrimination or blame.

- Work with mentors. Choose people with more "experience, strength and hope." They have gone before us and succeeded at things we are attempting to accomplish. This makes them a valuable asset. Appreciate their knowledge without expecting perfection.

- Talk with those you trust and ask for their feedback. Here is a great opportunity for stepping beyond your fear. Many of us believe that people will not like us if they really know us. Now is the opportunity to expel that myth by carefully revealing ourselves to trustworthy people.

- Continue to develop your skills and practice new behaviors in relationship to your health. With repeated attempts, some changes are bound to stick. Twelve-step programs ask members to bring their bodies first so sound thoughts and actions will follow. As one friend put it, "If heaven were only for the righteous, what would be its need?"

- Decide to change one new thing in relationship to your health each week. Add one more fresh fruit or vegetable to your diet each day. Drink one more 8-ounce glass of water each day. Do ten minutes of meditation each morning or evening. Take a daily fifteen-minute walk each day on your break, lunch hour, or before (after) work.

- Ironically, learn to take care of yourself rather than relying on others to do it for you. Expanding your support system may be useful. One person cannot always be there for you. Understand that your therapist, your doctor, a friend you work out with, or anyone else you depend upon to continue your healthy habits, will not always be available when you need them. Ensure continued success by having more individuals to check in with and to confide in about your progress.

CHAPTER 3

Stage Three: *Power Bar*

Please answer the questions in the following checklist:

Yes No

❏ ❏ Are you a competitive person?

❏ ❏ Do you try to appear in control or confidant?

❏ ❏ Do you have a need to prove yourself?

❏ ❏ Do you view power as a finite resource, that there may not be enough to go around?

❏ ❏ Do you feel inclined to have to use your knowledge?

❏ ❏ Do you understand the "rules of the game" in terms of personal appearance and community social norms?

Yes No

❏ ❏ Do you feel that you have reached your goals?

❏ ❏ Do you ask yourself first, "How will this affect me?"

❏ ❏ Do you feel there are winners and losers in life?

❏ ❏ Do you think that being thin, beautiful, strong, sexy, high energy, or athletic makes you more loveable, more acceptable, or a better person?

❏ ❏ Do you believe that maintaining a certain image allows you to control others?

If you answer "Yes" to many of these questions, it indicates that you align yourself with stage three.

WHAT IS STAGE THREE?

Stage three is the contemporary success stage where we reach our health goals, are proud of them, and enjoy being noticed for them. We worked hard to stop smoking, lose weight, and become fit. We feel good and we want it to show.

STAGE THREE INGREDIENTS

The characteristics are:

- Reaching goals and having others notice is important. External signs of success are seen as images of worthiness. These include such assets as being physically fit, winning competitions, having a good tan, having a great haircut, wearing the right clothes, being on the popular diet, going to the right yoga master, or belonging to the prestigious health club.

- Knowing the rules. Threes know the rules and will share them with others. Threes are often in positions of authority such as owners or managers of health clubs, treatment dependency units, human resource departments, employee assistance programs, nutrition stores, multi-level marketing organizations, and other health related businesses. A stage three person may be the constant athletic competitor, the spokesperson for non-profit agencies, the interviewed researcher, or the quoted medical expert. They also can be the successful business person who has the private health club membership, plays golf at the most prestigious course, can get tickets to the top sports events, and feels in control of their life.

- Being knowledgeable. Threes accumulate a lot of information about themselves, others, and the "how tos" for being healthy. They are able to supply information and often will. Sometimes they are financially rewarded well for their information. Or they are the resident expert and acknowledged as such.

- Feeling confidant that goals can be accomplished. These are the high-driven and "stick with it" folks. These "get going when the going gets tough" people attain many of their goals and know they can go even farther. They are self-assured based on their past experience with success and they know that they are "worth it."

WHAT HOLDS US BACK?

The "misfortune cookies" of this stage are:

- Ego—Needing to be right or to be perfect. You worked hard to reach your goal and you want to examine everything from the perspective of how it affects you. Threes feel in control. They have persisted and mastered their obstacles.

- Although stage threes are confident, their confidence can be a drawback. The very nature of being self-reliant can interfere with trusting there is a larger plan. The high-driven nature that assisted people to reach the peak of their current circumstances may prevent them from seeing their world from a larger perspective.

- Confusion and disillusionment—You have reached the top of your health goals. You are the fitness guru, the triathlon competitor, or the right body proportion. But something seems to be missing. This is a confusing time. Spiritual growth often appears difficult while in the middle of it. The good news is that we usually feel so much better once we get to the other side of these opportunities for growth.

- Competitive environments set up a win-lose paradigm. We see ourselves as being on one side or the other. There is much to be gained or to be lost. Physical discomfort here includes the organs of digestion. These organs are the most closely aligned with our emotions. From the time we are born, we experience the world through food and the stimulation of the mouth, stomach, and intestines. An emotional reaction to an event will actually send a response through our nerves to tighten around the intestines. We literally have a gut reaction.

WHAT PROMOTES CHANGE?

- A willingness to examine our personal inventory. This is called taking a fourth and fifth step in twelve-step circles. It could be a personal assessment in a therapeutic setting. We do the work while using the assistance of other, more objective individuals. I often joke that taking someone else's inventory is more accurate and more fun than taking my own. An inventory is an exact listing and acknowledgement of the desirable and undesirable traits in the person being reviewed. Much like the inventory of a business, each of us has items we wish to keep, sell, or store. We also have items we need to discard.

- Taking an accurate inventory requires a willingness to be honest. Additionally, it requires reviewing the items for discard with a dispassion. While these items may have served a useful purpose in the past, they now are expendable. In fact, retaining them will prevent our moving forward.

- Seeing these expendable items without judgment and releasing them through a variety of methods, frees us to move toward a moral place. Morality here is not right or wrong as detailed by a community, country, or organization. It is the internal peace that comes from knowing our own values. When we violate our own morality, we live in discomfort inside ourselves. This is called being "irritable, restless, and discontented" for some; being in dis-ease for others. It means we are not living comfortably in our own skin. This process plays host to countless physical discomforts and conditions.

- Doing an inventory does not put us in any particular stage. The motivation for doing the inventory may, however. If you are assessing your life because you want to please or appease others, you are in stage one (other dependent) or two (emulating mentors, sponsors, or perceived experts for their or others' approval). If you are doing it to honor your spiritual commitment to yourself and want everyone to know you have completed this assignment, then you are probably in stage three. If you are doing this to make sincere amends, to move forward and to "practice these principles in all our affairs," you are likely in stage four.

- People who are stuck at steps four and five in recovery circles, usually are having trouble shifting from stage three to stage four. Four requires reflection and a sincere willingness to be open to the possibilities beyond our own control.

- Stages have ambivalent transitions. Being willing to do something and wanting (liking) to do it are different things. There are many approaches that can be helpful with reflection. Journaling is great for keeping track of the journey toward successful change. Other approaches, such as artistic endeavors or silent retreats, may be helpful as well.

STAGE THREE STORIES

Mary Ellen is a high-powered businesswoman who suffered from severe constipation. She also feared using anyone else's bathroom. In fact, this fear manifested itself so strongly that she refused to have a bowel movement until she returned home from work each night. She would not travel because she did not want to be away from her home for very long. Feeling more fatigued and ill as time went on, Mary Ellen finally decided to seek counseling. As she dealt with various emotional issues, she began to let go of the toxic build up of the past—literally and figuratively.

Carl, a dynamo, superb athlete, and the owner of a successful business, had it all. Around his fortieth birthday, however, things changed dramatically in his life. His stepson's addiction to drugs became increasingly destructive to the entire family. Carl and his wife became estranged and their fifteen-year marriage ended. Business suffered, and Carl was baffled by the turn of events. Perfectionism, chronic worry, and stress set the stage for ulcers by reducing helpful hormones in the intestines. The unprotected intestinal lining was ripe for disease.

WHERE DO WE GO FROM HERE?
HOW DO WE MOVE TO STAGE FOUR?

Try these suggestions:

- Quiet reflection. Confusion subsides with practiced meditation. Move away from your distractions. Turn off the television, the beeper, and the cell phone. Better yet, take yourself out of your everyday environment and go someplace peaceful and calm. Many retreat facilities are becoming available, as are meditation centers. Your religious or spiritual community may offer classes or spiritual services as well.

- Creative indulgence. Allow yourself to try new things to enhance your sense of internal calm and to expand your view of the possibilities. Try a new exercise program, learn a new sport, or take a new cooking class. Travel and sample only the local cuisine, instead of familiar franchise offerings. Experiment with life in new ways.

- Commitment to honesty. As Miquel Luis Ruiz states in *The Four Agreements*, "Be impeccable in your world." Integrate what you do, what you say, and who you are.

- Perceive reality without judgment. Acceptance and surrender to what *is* opens the door to what *can be*. It is the resistance to the present circumstances that holds us hostage in time.

- Become aligned morally with your values. Learn who you are and how you need to live your life to be aligned with your principles. This benefits everyone. Shakespeare said, "To thine own self be true." The tag line on this is "and therefore, be false to no man."

- Meet and cultivate relationships with stage four, five, and six people. Learn from their experience, not to emulate them, but to experience your process of change, transcendence, and enlightenment. Stage four and five people are often good mentors. Look for experienced, selfless teachers. Stage six people may be more invisible and require us to use patient observation and present-time consciousness to notice them.

- Release expectations. Enjoy the endless possibilities that the world has to offer. Often, our life requests are to a lesser God. We bargain and negotiate, while a higher power is willing to give us so much more. Be open and willing to accept the abundance of your life.

CHAPTER 4

Stage Four: *Food Fasts*

Please answer the questions in the following checklist:

Yes No

❏ ❏ Are you proud of your work ethic, your knowledge, and your health?

❏ ❏ Are you always sponsoring or mentoring others?

❏ ❏ Does your internal life feel different from your external life?

❏ ❏ Do you choose to act with integrity?

❏ ❏ Do you think beyond the current areas of your personal and professional world?

❏ ❏ Is it important for you to have your own personal style?

❏ ❏ Can you admit mistakes without shame?

If you answer "Yes" to many of these questions, it indicates that you align yourself with stage four.

WHAT IS STAGE FOUR?

Stage four is the time to value our connections to others. It is also a time to be grateful for our individual uniqueness. Stage four people are often chosen as mentors, sponsors, and spiritual guides. People and animals alike are drawn to their integrity, continued competence, and solid experience with ageless health practices such as eating well, looking and being healthy, and treating themselves and others with respect.

This stage also asks the question, "What now?" Stage fours are caught between the competence of the past and the internal shift to expand to a new level. They want to integrate the confident external image to their speculative internal questions. They are on a path to wholeness.

STAGE FOUR INGREDIENTS

The characteristics are:

- Competence. Stage four people have proven that they are well versed in their area of expertise. They have been the competent athlete, the fitness guru, the one who lost and maintained their weight successfully over the years, the organic farmer, the person that never gets sick, the food co-op manager, the health food store owner, the meditation facilitator, the martial arts master, the televised healthcare personality, the yoga instructor, the accomplished author on menopause, osteoporosis and heart health, or the corporate stress management trainer.

- Mentorship. Stage fours are competent and trustworthy. This makes them more likely to have access to valuable resources and information for those who are drawn to them. People share openly with them and receive an abundant return for their time. Fours are fair, objective, and supportive. This makes them good models to emulate. Since they recently occupied a position similar to those they mentor and sponsor, fours can empathize with the difficulties of previous stages.

- Leadership. Stage four people practice solid leadership. They are sure of themselves and are willing to expand their boundaries. The best spiritual facilitators share their truth and encourage each person to gather what they need at their individual stage. I have heard excellent stage four facilitators utter simple statements, yet cover many levels of understanding for the participants. For example, a stage four mentor may talk of service work and its benefits to givers and receivers alike. A stage one person may hear the statement as hope for change. A stage two person may take notes on how to incorporate this information so that they can develop skills. A late stage three person may hear the statement as an eye-opening call to personal growth and redirection in life.

- Good students. Fours know that their teachers are everywhere. Fours learn to follow as well as to lead by staying open to the mentors' lessons.

- Reflection and balance. Although it is not visible to others, an internal battle often is being fought at stage four. There is a wonderful balance to be found between giving up the illusion of control and the acceptance of being human. The surrender of control and the acceptance of being yourself are the challenges and the rewards for stage four.

- Strength. Fours are robust individuals. They are seen as strong even though they may feel vulnerable inside. They have developed compassionate self-esteem and are learning to release their egos and their need to control.

- Separation from the status quo when appropriate. Stage four people have found their own style regarding health whether it be a flu shot, organic food, workout routine, spiritual practice, or eating pattern. The latest trend or health scare does not influence them unduly. Fours choose accordingly by exercising common sense and sound personal judgment. Then they move on to what they perceive to be more important issues.

WHAT HOLDS US BACK?

The "misfortune cookies" of this stage are:

- Ego and control. This is different from stage three. Stage threes are at the top and want to maintain their status. Stage four people spend their lives developing their expertise and personal style. Now they are thinking that there is something more in life. Fours must let go of ego, planning, and the need to "know" to answer the burning internal question, "What is my purpose in life?" The confusion between stages here may draw stage four people back to an earlier, more familiar stage and set of life patterns. This is the stage where relapse for an addiction or a return to harmful eating habits or lifestyle may bear the most associated feelings of shame. Stage fours believe they should "know better" and find their return to an earlier set of unfulfilling behaviors baffling.

- Not knowing our purpose in life. Stage fours need to ask why they are alive and how they can better serve others. This is not done from a codependent reference point. Rather the passion here stems from gaining knowledge of one's true purpose and having strength, courage, and persistence to follow through with that awareness.

• The physical price paid for ignoring the need to integrate ourselves and to move to the next stage is cardiovascular disease, respiratory illnesses, and cancer of the lungs and breasts.

WHAT PROMOTES CHANGE?

• A crisis of ego is the impetus here. Perhaps you have a chronic illness, acquired a disability, were involved in an accident, lost a loved one, lost your job, were financially hit by stock market losses, manifested a family disease, showed signs of aging, or realized you were middle-aged. In my late 30s I finally figured out that if I took my family's average life expectancy, adjusted for my risk reducing behaviors, and divided this number by two, that I would have the mid-point of my life, alias "middle-age." I suddenly realized that I was finishing the first half of my life!

- An imbalance between external competence and internal peace. Fours must give up the illusion of control, practice surrender to their spiritual shift, and accept their humanness. This embraces "life on life's terms."

STAGE FOUR STORIES

Twenty-four years ago, I decided to quit smoking. Four years and many serious attempts later I finally went cold turkey for the last time. One of the things that happened in that first year of abstinence was that I gained forty pounds. I had never been heavy at any previous time in my life, and I was unaccustomed to having to think in terms of being overweight. Being an athlete, I always enjoyed a strong, healthy body. Now I was considerably heavier and I could not lose the extra pounds no matter what I did. I could have used this as a good reason to relapse and to resume smoking. I chose to accept the situation and to stick with my abstinence. A year later, by retaining my good eating and exercising habits, my body metabolism normalized and the weight came off. By continuing to choose healthy behaviors and seeing the process through to the end, I was able to be successful with my abstinence and health.

Many recovering individuals tell their stories of personal crisis and spiritual awakenings. The stories often include incredible self-abusive behavior and a final accumulation of events and emotions known as "hitting one's bottom." One gentleman, John, related the following story. He drank heavily and was suicidal. He walked off of an 80-foot cliff and was discovered the next morning by the railroad workers in the rail yard below. Despite bruises and pain, he had not broken a single bone. More surprisingly, he walked away from the incident. He told me they sent him to a detoxification unit. While there he asked a local volunteer if she thought God had another plan for him. Today, ten years later, he knows that God does have a plan for him and that it is still unfolding. He divides his time between his family, his job, and his service work.

Betty contemplated whether to join a multi-level marketing organization because she used and liked the results of their nutritional products. She also believed the products were not useful for everyone, however, and wanted to have a broader based business. She decided to join the organization and to market theirs and other product lines according to the perceived needs of her clients. Her clients, in turn, saw her as having their best interests at heart and helped her business grow.

WHERE DO WE GO FROM HERE?
HOW DO WE MOVE TO STAGE FIVE?

Try these suggestions:

- Carve out quiet moments and develop spiritual practices that include reflection, prayer, and meditation. Spiritual retreats are very useful to gain insights on our life purpose and the pathway to achieve it. As we quiet the mind, our purpose and future actions become clearer, almost effortlessly.

- Take responsibility for your life. We may have been abused as a child, raised by an alcoholic adult, battered by an unloving partner, disabled by an unforeseen event, or tortured by the paranoia and paralyzing fear of a mental health disease. Whatever the situation, we must forgive others, forgive ourselves, and allow our life to move forward. Taking responsibility for our own life is not the same as excusing others' behaviors nor pretending those behaviors did not cause pain. By taking responsibility today for our reactions to those events and our emotions, we have the greatest chance of moving beyond the past and the pain.

- Forgive others. True amends require accepting the human experience. We are all interconnected. The spirit of this process involves honestly acknowledging our own actions and motivations for past behaviors. We provide restitution where necessary, not from fear or a need to please, but from a willingness to love others and ourselves. The gift of truly forgiving my ex-husband offered many benefits. I was able to see my part in the past, began to be merciful with myself, and was able to move forward with my life. This released me from grief, anger, and the health issues they can cause.

- Expect a crisis of ego and letting go. At this stage, we are challenged from the inside. As the old Pogo cartoon stated, "We have seen the enemy and it is us." If we continue our spiritual practices, this too shall pass.

- Grieve. Change, even helpful change, means letting go. To say "yes" to something new means to say "no" to something else. Choosing a new pathway does not negate our human reaction to grieve.

- Let go. Grief is the human emotion associated with change. Ironically, impermanence is the silver lining of life. Without change and transformation we would never experience life. Plants would not grow to provide food. The seasons would not vary to provide harvest. You would not gain new skills for health and wellness.

CHAPTER 5

Stage Five: *Gourmet Dining*

Please answer the questions in the following checklist:

Yes No

❏ ❏ Do you care about others' health as much as you do about your own?

❏ ❏ Do you think that other people's opinions of you are none of your business?

❏ ❏ Are you unaffected by the reactions of others to you or your ideas?

❏ ❏ Does your life purpose reach beyond your immediate world?

❏ ❏ Are you deeply spiritual?

❏ ❏ Do you enjoy time alone?

❏ ❏ Do you give away what you have learned and accomplished to empower others?

Yes   No

❏   ❏   Do you usually feel a sense of internal calm?

❏   ❏   Do you feel that there are no "big deals" in life?

❏   ❏   Do you believe in abundance?

❏   ❏   Do you laugh at yourself?

If you answer "Yes" to many of these questions, it indicates that you align yourself with stage five.

WHAT IS STAGE FIVE?

Stage five is a crossover stage. There are no gurus, masters, or techniques to get us here. It is a personal journey to find your intuitive self.

STAGE FIVE INGREDIENTS

The characteristics are:

- Self-acceptance. Stage fives accept their humanness and their reality. They acknowledge their strengths and their limits. Continued improvement is not a mandate for themselves, although the willingness to change is always there.

- Calmness. There is an internal calm at this stage even during times of stressful situations. There is contentment with life that underlies and highlights everything.

- Provocative questions. Stage five people ask challenging questions without malice. They are our hopeful collective conscious. What is the impact of genetically altered food? Should we use antibiotics in the food industry? What will the future needs of healthcare entail and how will we provide this? What is my company's contribution to preserving the environment? What is my responsibility to contribute to the rest of the world? What is my responsibility to protect future generations? Many native cultures believe that every decision made should benefit, or at least do no harm, to the next seven generations. The question for a stage five person is, "How do my decisions and actions affect others?"

- Humbleness. Fives release their egos and are able to transfer their energy away from personal problems and concerns to other people, organizations, cultures, countries, and ideas.

- Empathy. Fives see the world in realistic terms. They can engage the world with peace, calm, and joy, not because they are in denial, but because they accept the shades of gray in life. Our popular media may display supermodels as a beauty standard, or millionaire CEOs as power symbols, but accepting our genetics, physical attributes, and life situations leads to sustained internal beauty. One of the most enlightened prayers I have ever heard is the adapted serenity prayer often quoted in recovery programs. "God grant me the serenity to accept the things I cannot change, the courage to change the things I can, and the wisdom to know the difference."

- Empower with stories. Stage five people are often almost invisible. They possess knowledge, a balanced view of the world, and a wish to empower others. They will often do this through story-telling rather than direct forms of leadership. In fact, they will often be reluctant leaders. You can find fives in the teams of healthcare organizations, the individual practitioner, the old-timer in recovery, and the everyday person sharing their "experience, strength, and hope."

• Understand life purpose. Fives know why they are here. They integrate their entire life to this purpose. For example, a stage five person may anonymously help develop a neighborhood clinic or provide expertise for the development of a nutritional product without ever being recognized for it. Or they may be a famous person who, having reached success in the material world, decides to give back on another level in gratitude for all they received.

• Spiritual nature. We are all spiritual beings. Stage five people live their spirituality in all aspects of their lives. The particular form does not matter. In the late 1980s, I traveled to Thailand. While visiting one of the many Buddhist temples, I asked one of the caretakers why the temple and its stunning, gigantic Buddha statue were both built with wood. I asked if they feared its eventual deterioration. His reply was, "Form is impermanent and does not matter; the principles will live forever."

WHAT HOLDS US BACK?

The "misfortune cookies" of this stage are:

- Inflexibility. Fives will get stuck with rigid rules or dogma. An ability to slip outside of the box, to see the world from many, equally important, perspectives is necessary here. An unwillingness to acquire flexibility and to see beyond our own beliefs and experiences is called the "wall" in Janet Hagberg's Real Power model. Many of us will not cross from stage four to five by choice. We know what is required of us, but choose not to follow that path.

- Loss of direction. Spiritual growth often is not easy. A few years ago, I struggled with what I called a low-grade depression for a year. Everything looked gray, flat, and two-dimensional. There were no specific events triggering this sadness. Oddly enough, I knew this would pass, and I continued my spiritual practices. A year later the feeling lifted, and I became more alive and passionate about my work than ever. I now know the experience was a form of spiritual growth, a time of inner reflection and renewal.

- Loss of faith. This is one of the hardest things. To lose faith is more difficult than to never have found it in the first place. The disillusionment and grief can be overwhelming when this happens. Many people have a "dark night of the soul" in their past. Perhaps a life choice results in ambivalence. This is a time for inner reflection and eventual emergence as a renewed spiritual being.

- Physical challenges at this stage include diseases of the thyroid, the throat, neck, esophagus, teeth and gums. When people are holding themselves back or afraid to know and say who they are, this can manifest in laryngitis, reflux, or a stiff neck.

WHAT PROMOTES CHANGE?

- Change is encountered as we begin to not only see paradoxes in life, but also begin to internally accept them as the way of the universe. Movement forward, for personal gain, does not matter.

- Spiritual challenges. The old way of doing things just does not work anymore. We are challenged internally to grow and to serve. We cannot ignore this pull toward our destiny any longer.

STAGE FIVE STORIES

Kate was in her thirties and had to stop running 10K races and marathons because of knee problems. She agonized over this because she was not getting the benefit of endorphins from her running, plus she was gaining weight. This state of limbo became very frustrating and depressing for her. During her year of rehabilitation she began to pray, meditate, and search for a personal serenity connected to her changed circumstances. I ran into her ten years later. She is now the manager of a retreat house. She gave up her hectic, high-powered job, makes considerably less money, and is completely at peace.

Another example involves the work and commitment of a spiritual and recovering community at the Peace Valley Hot Springs (retreat, hotel, and bed and breakfast facility) in Boulder, Montana. Various spiritual leaders, therapists, social workers, and everyday people began working together to examine their lives in recovery, not only as individuals, but also as a community. I am fortunate enough to have lived with, worked with, and learned from many of these people over the last seventeen years. Some of these people continue to live at this renovated turn-of-the-century hotel in the Deer Lodge Forest. Others live in various places all over the world. They offer support to those who want to honestly examine and modify their lives around many dependencies, including dysfunction with food, relationships, and other ingestive or process addictions. The elders in these communities are sometimes, but not always, poor from a material point of view, yet wealthy in wisdom and spiritual centeredness.

WHERE DO WE GO FROM HERE?
HOW DO WE MOVE TO STAGE SIX?

This stage begins to become more difficult to describe in terms of movement strategies. Less tangible things such as deep, internalized spirituality and a faith beyond our current experience become paramount here. Life is less predictable in stage six. We must be willing to let go of the assurances of the past with one hand, while not yet grasping something new to sustain us with the other hand. Stage six is truly the leap-of-faith stage. Few are willing to risk things, people, past beliefs, and all the old attachments in life to grow into the selfless, spiritual beings of stage six.

Letting go is particularly hard in the area of nutrition. Food has many emotional properties associated with it. There is the familiar concept of comfort food and Mom's home cooking. Chicken soup and chest ointment still conjour up the image of me being taken care of as a sick child. This vision remains despite the fact that we were not usually given chicken soup when sick.

Food also has physiological and psychological properties associated with it. Sugar will give quick energy and expansiveness to people. Salt will help ground people. The industrial strength latte provides a quick boost to weary workers every day. It also is a diuretic and an acidic compound digestively. This has various side affects associated with it such as dehydration and the loss of minerals and other nutrients from the body. Hydration needs to be increased to offset some of these affects. I have seen people choose reflux and stomach disorder medications rather than consider abstaining from caffeine. They are not even willing to drink more water every day, despite the fact that this will often help their symptoms and their health in general. The power of food is multi-dimensional. Giving up the familiar comfort of an early morning latte or a late night snack of ice cream is hard when we are facing the unknown reward of altering our habits. It takes a leap of faith.

CHAPTER 6

Stage Six: *Soul Food*

Please answer the questions in the following checklist:

Yes No

❏ ❏ Do you accept yourself as you are?

❏ ❏ Do you accept others as they are?

❏ ❏ Do you see the interconnectedness of all things?

❏ ❏ Is service to the world and individuals your greatest interest?

❏ ❏ Do you operate on an internal set of values and "practice these principles in all your affairs?"

❏ ❏ Are you unafraid of death?

❏ ❏ Would you sacrifice your life for your life purpose?

Yes No

❏ ❏ Are you committed to life, yet detached from particular outcomes?

❏ ❏ Do you feel complete peace inside?

❏ ❏ Are you considered wise?

❏ ❏ Are you sought after for advice even though you do not have formal power such as a title or position?

❏ ❏ Do you enjoy solitude and silence?

❏ ❏ Do you ask the unanswerable questions without being precocious?

❏ ❏ Do you see the whole picture?

"Yes" answers indicate that you may align yourself with stage six. Caution is encouraged here since most people do not wish to be as selfless as a true stage six person. Stage six people are fearless, humble, accepting of present circumstance, accepting of death, and willing to embrace the paradox called life.

WHAT IS STAGE SIX?

Sixes are wise. They are not totally available at all times because they choose to spend much of their time alone in silent reflection. This recharging time is necessary to connect to their source and to be totally present and available when engaging with others. They see the whole picture, knowing that the individual factors are less than the synergy of the whole. Judgment is unnecessary. To be or not to be is not the question for sixes. Existence is a continuation of ever-changing form that may or may not manifest in the physical world.

For example, the glorious sun is at the middle of the solar system. This is true whether it is beaming down on us or hidden behind the gray thunderheads. The brown and weathered grass lies unseen beneath the winter snowdrift waiting for the spring thaw and renewed growth.

At the same time, everything that exists is ever changing. The lemongrass candle burns, and does not have the same flame as a second ago.

The oxygen and wax that feed it are different, yet the flame continues. Similarly, Little Crab Lake's northern water today is not the same water that we swam in September, yet the lake is still there.

Sometimes the essence of some thing or some body may not manifest in this physical world because of the rule of inter-being which states, "Everyone and everything is related to everything else." The flame that burns does so because its universal mates were available for this to happen. The paraffin wax, the oxygen rich air, and a sulfur match permitted the flame to manifest from the candle. Stage sixes understand and accept these principles. Health and physical being are honored within the context of acceptance for the world as it is. There is an unworried indifference for meeting physical, often arbitrary, beauty standards. Finally there is a reverence to respect all, including ourselves, as we lead moderate and healthy lives. Beauty is truly more than skin deep as realized in a calm presence and peace of mind.

We may all have some stage six in us from time to time. Stage six people live congruently in this stage. They are not influenced by the status quo, but rather by their internal knowing, which is never self-destructive nor harmful to others.

STAGE SIX INGREDIENTS

The characteristics are:

- Stage six people are comfortable with contradictions in life. There is no right or wrong way. There are options from which they can choose. Better yet, sixes enjoy asking questions more than they enjoy getting answers. Ambiguity does not bother them. Stage six people will live with the following paradoxes:

- Things can be simple, but they are not necessarily easy.

- Our strength is our weakness; our weakness is our strength.

- Commitment to life, self, and others means detachment.

- Everything is interrelated, yet separate.

- Physical concerns are significant, yet insignificant.

- Health is out of reverence for the present, yet dying is of no consequence.

- Sixes have no fear of death. There is no fear of their or others' deaths. Physical health is maintained to experience life. It is also sustained so that they can continue to serve others.

- Sixes have no fear of losing physical youth, strength, and beauty. Their beauty is internal and eternal. It draws others to them from a different source. Standards of beauty and youth are known to them, yet acknowledgement for these things have no significance to a six.

- Life is purpose. Stage six people appear similar to stage one people in that they appear to be doing very little to move their own lives ahead. Their life inspiration and passion come from within. Sixes have little need for material possession or physical attractiveness. Prior experiences or internal spiritual shifts provided another perspective on life. A near death experience, or the death of a loved one, may have been crucial toward their transformation and re-evaluation of life's priorities. They are not attached to a particular aspect of life, but rather to service itself.

- Service with gratitude, not attitude. Stage six people may be well known, but often are not. They do not crave, nor need, recognition for their efforts. They do not do things from a need to feel good. In fact, they have no attachment to their deeds at all. The source for inspiration and action flows through them, transcending them, regardless of circumstances and situation.

- Unerring ethics. Sixes have the ability to call things as they see them. They may be an advocate for products or services that they believe will benefit others the most, yet be unwilling to verbally support anything that appears to be available solely for the greed or ego of themselves or another. Health products abound. Stage six people would be a Ralph

Nader of the health world, exposing fraud without malice and sponsoring beneficial options without needing to be rewarded financially or otherwise on a personal level. They do not fear the judgment of the status quo because they do not need to be recognized for their beliefs or actions.

- Unexplainable knowing. Stage six people know things through methods that the rest of us may not experience. They use their own personal history, and they tap into the universe for their truth. They may not even be able to explain how they know these things.

WHAT HOLDS US BACK?

The "misfortune cookies" of this stage are:

- Being human. One of my favorite recovery speakers states, "No matter how well you practice the spiritual principles of the twelve-step program, you will never rise above being a basic human being." As human animals we are a complex mix of emotions, spirit, and physical attributes. Our genetics and the environment have influences on us beyond our intellect and scientific knowledge.

• Unique but part of a greater whole. We are unique, yet comprised of the seeds of our ancestors and the hope of our future generations. Just as women will follow their mothers' menopausal patterns and men may follow their family's historical hair loss, we are predisposed to certain physical and emotional realities such as family disease and physical appearance. These are often our greatest spiritual teachers, though, and can be cherished for our transcendence spiritually.

WHAT PROMOTES CHANGE?

Human reality is the force for change and transformation here. Stage six people that I met or studied almost always had a life-changing experience that provided a different view of the world. Once this previously unknown view became apparent, options abounded and the blinding wall of ignorance disappeared forever. I will often hear people in recovery groups and in other spiritual communities make statements about this phenomenon. Once they have been exposed to a new truth about their situation (i.e. eating disorder, overeating patterns, food plan, personal moral code), people are never able to return to their previously destructive patterns with impunity. As one recovering alcoholic said, "It ruins your next drunk." They do not even have to fully internalize this new view for the change to occur. That is the beauty and the mystery of spiritual experience and transformation. It is a wonderful and evolving process.

STAGE SIX STORIES

I do not consider myself to be a stage six person and, like many others, I relate to some of the attributes of this stage. About ten summers ago, I worked at a turn-of-the-century hotel in the mountains of Montana's Deer Lodge Forest. We welcomed various groups to the hotel for retreats. One of these groups was a group of ritual abuse survivors. I provided various services including therapeutic massage. As I worked on the various individuals, I discovered that I could determine when they were about to go into a flashback before it actually occurred. At first this was a bewildering and frightening experience for me. I never fully understood how I knew these things, but I continued my work anyway. I experienced a spiritual shift and no longer cared how I knew. I used the information to keep my clients safe during the stressful and often physical flashbacks. I believe a big part of that was my readiness to realize that I had these gifts. I also know that by embracing this part of me, I was able to interact with this group. I admired and learned from these people. They had been through so many horrifying experiences in the past, and were still willing to trust another human being in such a vulnerable way. I was deeply moved by their persistence of faith in love and the human spirit.

On another occasion, I lived in Los Angeles in the early 1990s. One morning I awoke to a gentle rolling motion. It felt like I was on a boat, but I was on land. I knew immediately that it was an earthquake. The next thing I knew, the bed began moving across the floor while the windows shook uncontrollably. As the bed moved, I heard a voice in my head say with absolute calm and certainty, "You are not going to die today." Despite the chaos around me, I felt entirely at peace and unafraid. The whole event lasted less than a minute, but felt like an eternity. I spent the rest of the day walking at the beach and around Los Angeles. Buildings had collapsed, people had been killed, and main highway arteries had been decimated. Despite aftershocks, I felt free from fear in a city that was very afraid. I have experienced absolute fearlessness and a sense of internal peace a few times since then. It is marvelous!

Others have lived their epiphanies too. I am privileged to work with many clients who examine their options around a physical or emotional concern. Dan, a post cancer patient, had treatment for leukemia and survived a long year plus rehabilitation. After two years of remission, his disease returned. I asked Dan if he was planning on repeating the treatment. He said, "No. I always feared I would get cancer. I got cancer and survived it. Now I have cancer again and I have no fear of dying. I simply do not want to repeat the misery of the last year. I want to enjoy the rest of my life, living it one day at a time. Perhaps I will feel differently tomorrow, but this is how I feel at the moment." He never repeated treatment and is still alive and thriving.

Kathy, a friend of mine in Canada, was diagnosed with ovarian cancer. I moved back to the United States and could not be with her through much of her journey. I did make a trip back to Vancouver, though, while she was going through one of her many surgeries. She was weary, but oddly at peace. She told me that she was ready to go. She had taken care of all the loose ends for her finances and her children. She made peace with her family. She was tired of the hospital surgeries and wanted to leave this physical reality. I was deeply struck by the calm that surrounded her and was grateful to share that last moment with her. She died within a year of her diagnosis. I was unable to be with her, yet I shall never forget her laughter, her graceful dancing, our walks on Kitsilano Beach in Vancouver, or a million other memories.

A final story involves the recovery of an individual, Brianne. She was at the end of her destructive disease and was going to get sober or die. Being suicidal, she examined her pain and a possible suicide attempt, trying to determine if life and its challenges were really worth the effort. All at once she had the experience of a voice within her head saying, "Do you want to die?" This voice was internal yet separate from her. It was a non-judgmental voice. Brianne experienced the question as a neutral request. She interpreted the voice to be asking if she wanted help dying or help living. The implied assumption was that the voice would help her whichever way she decided. It became immediately clear to her she did not want to die, but she could no longer continue living her life as she had been. She began to make changes that impacted her life beneficially for more than a decade.

WHERE DO WE GO FROM HERE?

Try these suggestions:

- If you are a stage six person, you probably are not reading this book. You also may not be taking any quizzes or looking to understand this stage. You have already accepted your life and your life purpose whether there is intellectual understanding or not. You are probably quietly serving others and living a peaceful life.

- The one exception here is the cyclical nature of life. People may acquire a certain stage, including stage six, and then repeat the cycle on a new level, perhaps for another aspect of one's life. For example, people who do not fear their own death, may wish to live longer to benefit their children or grandchildren. Paradoxically, stage six people also know that we are all connected whether physically alive or not. Therein lies the paradox and dilemma of being a "spiritual being having a human experience." May you resolve this with peace of mind and harmony of spirit.

If you have a personal story to share or would like to provide feedback on this book, please send your stories, comments, or suggestions to the following e-mail: **pat@patcasello.com**. If you are interested in receiving a courtesy monthly newsletter on health, healthy change, and wellness, sign up on **www.patcasello.com** or send a message to our e-mail. The website also offers information on Dr. Casello's teleclasses, seminars, and other products.

APPENDIX A

Adaptation of Janet Hagberg's Personal Power Model

Stage	One	Two
Stage Name	Fast Food	Community Buffet
Personal Power Definition	Powerlessness	Power by association
Ingredients	Fear; helplessness; egocentricity; distrust; lack of information; dependent; low self esteem.	Growing interest in self & skills; questions of faith; desire mentors; seeking a new environment; a sense of being "stuck."
Health Crisis Symptoms	Low back pain; fatigue; obesity; rectal, bowel & sexual dysfunction; depression.	Urinary, pelvic, low back, bowel, reproductive problems.
Misfortune Cookies (Shadow Side)	Fear; ego; loyalty to the status quo; lack of a "true" sense of honor.	Do it alone; stopping too soon; staying in a bad place; & constantly changing things.
Golden Shadow	Courage in the face of fear & the unknown; honesty.	Beginning to trust; letting go and re-examination.
Movement Forward	Raise self-esteem; increase knowledge, develop skills.	Build faith; work with mentors & continue skill development.

Continued

Stage	Three	Four
Stage Name	Power Bar	Food Fasts
Personal Power Definition	Power by symbols	Power by Reflection
Ingredients	External signs of success; realistic; knowledgeable; confident.	Competence; mentorship; leadership; good students; reflection; strength; status quo; separation.
Health Crisis Symptoms	Digestive organ disorders.	Heart & Lung diseases; lung & breast cancer.
Misfortune Cookies (Shadow Side)	Ego; confidence; intelligence; confusion; & dillusionment.	Ego; control; not knowing life purpose.
Golden Shadow	Take inventory; honesty; knowing own values; sincere amends; reflective; willing	Develop spiritually; be responsible for your life.
Movement Forward	Quiet reflection; creativity; honesty; no judgement; align "morally"; use mentors; no expectations.	Forgive; grieve; let go; develop spiritually; take responsibility.

Stage	Five	Six
Stage Name	Gourmet Dining	Soul Food
Personal Power Definition	Power by Purpose	Power by Gestalt
Ingredients	Self acceptance; calmness; provocative; questioners; humbleness; empathy; empowering; understand life purpose; spiritual.	Comfortable with paradoxes; no fear of death; no fear of aging; life is purpose; service w/ gratitude; unerring ethics; knowledge & wisdom.
Health Crisis Symptoms	Disease of thyroid; throat; neck; head; esophagus; teeth & gums.	Humanness; loss of internal peace.
Misfortune Cookies (Shadow Side)	Inflexibility; loss of direction; loss of faith.	Humanness; unique yet part of the whole.
Golden Shadow	See & accept paradoxes; spiritual challenges.	Human reality accepted; spiritual transformation & transcendence.
Movement Forward	Deep; internal spirituality; faith beyond experience.	Life changing experience.

RESOURCES

Alcoholics Anonymous World Services, Inc., Twelve Steps and Twelve Traditions, 1986

Alcoholics Anonymous World Services, Inc., *Alcoholics Anonymous, This is the Fourth Edition of the Big Book*, the Basic Text for Alcoholics Anonymous, 2001

Fox, Emmet, *The Sermon On The Mount*, Harper & Row, Publishers, New York, 1938.

Hagberg, Janet O., *Real Power, Stages of Personal Power in Organizations*, Winston Press, 2002

Hawkins, David R., M.D. Ph.D., *The Eye of the I, From Which Nothing is Hidden*, Veritas Publishing, 2001

Kirk, Dr. Constance C., *Taming the Diet Dragon, Using Language & Imagery for Weight Control & Body Transformation* (Llewellyn's Self-Empowerment), May 1994.

Myss, Caroline, Ph.D., *Anatomy of the Spirit, The Seven Stages of Power and Healing*, Three Rivers Press, New York, 1996.

Myss, Caroline, Ph.D., *Sacred Contracts, Awakening Your Divine Potential*, Harmony Books, New York, 2001.

Overeaters Anonymous, The Twelve Steps of Overeaters Anonymous, 1990.

Pitchford, Paul, *Healing with Whole Foods, Oriental Traditions and Modern Nutrition*, North Atlantic Books, Berkeley, California, 1993.

Ruiz, Michael Luis, *The Four Agreements: A Practical Guide to Personal Freedom*, Amber Allen Publishing.

Santillo, Humbart "Smokey", N.D., Ph.D., *Intuitive Eating*, Hohm Press, 1993.

Schulz, Mona Lisa, M.D., Ph.D., *Awakening Intuition*, Three Rivers Press, New York, 1998.

Schaef, Anne Wilson, *Beyond Therapy, Beyond Science: A New Model For Healing The Whole Person*, San Francisco, Harpercollins, 1992.

Thich Nhat Hanh, *no death, no fear, Comforting Wisdom for Life*, Riverhead Books, New York, 2002

Tolle, Eckhart, *Practicing The Power of Now, Essential Teachings, Meditations, And Exercises From The Power Of Now*, New World Library, Novato, California, 2001

Tolle, Eckart, *The Power of Now, A Guide To Spiritual Enlightenment*, New World Library, Novato, California, 1999.

Websites:
>   www.janethagberg.com
>   www.patcasello.com

Dr. Patricia M. Casello